Angels up high

A Children's Christmas Musical

Denis O'Gorman & Barry Hart

We hope you enjoy *Angels up high*. Further copies are available
from your local music shop or Christian bookshop.

In case of difficulty, please contact the publisher direct by writing to:

The Sales Department
KEVIN MAYHEW LTD
Buxhall
Stowmarket
Suffolk IP14 3BW

Phone 01449 737978
Fax 01449 737834
E-mail info@kevinmayhewltd.com

Please ask for our complete catalogue of outstanding Church Music.

First published in Great Britain in 2001 by Kevin Mayhew Ltd.

© Copyright 2001 Kevin Mayhew Ltd.

ISBN 1 84003 794 6
ISMN M 57004 914 1
Catalogue No: 1450226

0 1 2 3 4 5 6 7 8 9

Cover design by Jonathan Stroulger
Music setter: Donald Thomson
Proof reader: Linda Ottewell

Printed and bound in Great Britain

Cast

Mary
Angel Gabriel
Joseph
Caleb
Innkeeper
Reuben
Cook
Hazar
Hiram
Mr Zedechiah
Shemiah
Jozabad
Zabdiel
Captain Ezra-Hadid-Mattaniah
Hasshub
Akkub
Zabdi
Zerah
Servants to the Wise Men
Innkeeper's companions
Shepherds

ANGELS

Sunbeam
Gloria
Angelica
Twilight
Stardust
Moonshine
Rainbow

WISE MEN

Balthazar
Melchior
Caspar

SERVANTS

Igal
Nahbi
Palti
Raphu
Gaddi *(optional)*

Songs

ANGELS UP HIGH

Text and Lyrics: Denis O' Gorman
Music: Barry Hart

SCENE: NAZARETH

Enter MARY with clothes and bags. She begins to pack clothes into bags, as if for a journey. Enter ANGEL GABRIEL. After a few moments, MARY looks up, startled. ANGEL GABRIEL sings:

THE ANGEL GABRIEL'S SONG

1. Ma - ry, do not be a-fraid, I've come from God a-bove to
2. Ma - ry, do not be a-fraid, you'll ne - ver be a-lone, when

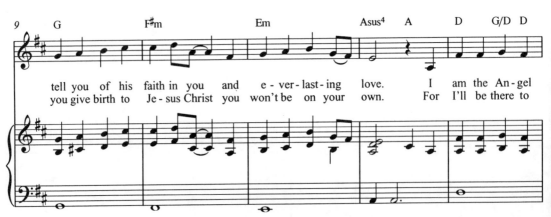

tell you of his faith in you and e - ver-last-ing love. I am the An - gel
you give birth to Je - sus Christ you won't be on your own. For I'll be there to

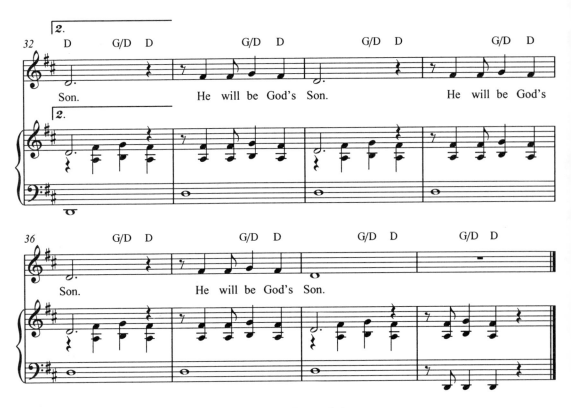

Exit ANGEL GABRIEL. MARY kneels in silence for a while.
Enter JOSEPH, who goes up to MARY slowly.

Joseph	*(gently)* Mary, I think it's time we should be leaving. It's a long way to Bethlehem.
Mary	Joseph, there's something I should tell you.
Joseph	*(kindly)* I know already. The Angel Gabriel appeared to me as well and told me in a dream.
Mary	*(softly and joyfully)* And *thousands* of holy angels will be there to protect us. Angels up high, carrying a star to Bethlehem.
Joseph	*(gently)* It will be a lovely sight, Mary. You have been blessed by God.
Mary	I am just a poor and lowly girl, but I shall do what God commands.
Joseph	Then let's go – under the guidance of his holy angels.

Exeunt MARY and JOSEPH.

SCENE: UP IN THE SKY

Enter ANGEL GABRIEL, gracefully. She looks offstage. The following dialogue, backstage, should give the audience the impression that the play has gone disastrously wrong from the start!

Sunbeam	Gloria, stop pushing me. You'll break my wings!

Gloria	Well, get out of my way! *I'm* supposed to be in front of you!
Sunbeam	No, you're not! You go behind *her!* I've got to carry the star.
Angelica	No, I'm supposed to carry the star. *You* take it from me later, when we get to Bethlehem!
Gabriel	*(sternly, to sidestage)* Come up here at once and stop all that fighting!

Enter ANGELS, quite ungracefully – pushing and shoving each other.
SUNBEAM carries the star.

Angelica	*(to ANGEL GABRIEL, whining)* You said *I* could carry the star after her!
Gabriel	You'll get your turn like everyone else. We'll sit here for a while and wait for the Wise Men to catch us up.

All ANGELS face the audience.

Twilight	*(to ANGEL GABRIEL)* Can we go down now? I've never been on earth before.
Gabriel	Not until we get to Bethlehem. Just stay there and do as you are told.
Stardust	I'm scared up here. I've never flown this high before.
Sunbeam	Don't be so silly! You're an angel. You can't fall out of the sky.
Stardust	*(spitefully to SUNBEAM)* I wish *you* would!
Gabriel	*(crossly, to all ANGELS)* That's enough now! You haven't stopped arguing and squabbling since we left heaven.
Moonshine	*(insolently)* All right, Gabriel. Just because you're an *Arch*angel. You don't have to be so bossy!
Gabriel	*(crossly, to MOONSHINE)* Look! One more word out of you and I'll send you straight back to heaven.
Moonshine	I don't care. I'd rather be in heaven. I didn't want to come in the first place!
Gabriel	Quiet, all of you! Not another word till the Wise Men arrive.

The first two verses of the following song are sung with exaggerated angelic innocence, while, at the same time, they give each other little pushes and shoves.

LITTLE ANGELS

At the end of the song, ANGELS freeze in various exaggerated positions. Pause, while ANGEL GABRIEL, hands on hips, surveys them in disbelief.

Gabriel   Will you sit down immediately!

ANGELS sit. Long pause, during which ANGELS become progressively more bored and mischievous.

Rainbow   This is *boring!* Why are they taking so long?

Gabriel   Because they're *humans*. They can't fly like us.

Angelica   *(grabs the star from SUNBEAM and begins to move)*
Come on, let's go. Let them find their own way to Bethlehem.

Gabriel   *(slowly and indignantly to ANGELICA)* Put down that star at once!
(ANGELICA hesitates, half-stubbornly, half-unsure) Go on, put it down.
(ANGELICA puts down the star, reluctantly) Right, from now on, no one touches that star until I say so.
(ALL sit again in silence for a while looking fed up.)

Angelica   *(grumpily)* I thought you said this trip would be fun.

Gabriel   *(firmly, but not shouting, matter-of-fact)* I thought I told you to keep quiet.
(ALL sit in silence.)

SCENE: DOWN BELOW IN THE DESERT

Enter SERVANTS, looking the worse for wear, clothes torn and dusty. They are struggling with heavy boxes.

Igal   *(relieved and gratefully dropping his box on the ground)*
Look, Nahbi, that star's disappeared! That means our journey is over!

Nahbi   *(excitedly, drops his box, exhausted)* This must be Palestine.

All SERVANTS put down their boxes with relief and wipe their brows.

Palti   At last, we'll see the new-born King!

Raphu   *(taking deep breaths, exhausted)* Phew, I'm glad about that.
I couldn't walk another mile!

Gaddi   Nor me, I'm ready to drop.

All SERVANTS sit on their boxes, quite shattered. They repeat words and phrases such as 'Oh, my feet!', 'Phew, at last we're here!' and 'I thought we'd never make it.' Enter three WISE MEN being 'carried' on chairs (if they walk between two poles held front and back, with richly decorated drapes reaching from floor to waist height, it will give the impression they are being carried). In complete contrast to the SERVANTS, the WISE MEN are dressed in beautiful silk robes. They look cool as other SERVANTS wave huge fans round them. The scene should give the impression that they have brought everything, bar the kitchen sink, for the comfort of the journey.

Balthazar	*(solemnly, raising his hand)* Wait! *(The SERVANTS look up. BALTHAZAR steps out of his 'chair')* Our journey is not yet over. We have many more miles to go. *(SERVANTS begin to groan and grumble)* But, have no fear. We shall see you through, even without the star to guide us.
Igal	But, sir, we can't go on. We really can't!
Balthazar	*(taking a grape from the bowl offered by a SERVANT)* Igal, in my book there is no such word! *(Pause, then confidently)* Sacrifice, honour, duty – yes. But no such word as 'can't'.

SCENE: UP IN THE SKY

Stardust	Cor, he thinks a lot of himself, doesn't he?
Gabriel	Just keep quiet, will you?

Down on the ground the SERVANTS are looking dejected and are grumbling amongst themselves.

Gloria	Can they see us from down there?
Angelica	Course not, stupid! We're invisible.

SCENE: DOWN ON THE GROUND

Melchior	*(to SERVANTS, solemnly)* Take courage, we shall find the new-born King, whatever the cost, whatever the sacrifice. Come trial or tribulation, we shall not flinch from our duty!
Caspar	*(confidently and solemnly)* So be brave, we're all in this together. We won't let you down!
Balthazar	But now we must rest for a while. It's been a long night and we've travelled far. *(to CALEB)* Caleb, perhaps you'd prepare us a simple meal. *(CALEB claps his hands and most of the SERVANTS scuttle off stage)*

Caleb   *(to BALTHAZAR)* I'll do my best, sir, but I'm afraid it won't be much.

MELCHIOR puts his arm round CALEB reassuringly. CASPAR and BALTHAZAR go frontstage and SERVANTS come forward with huge cushions on which the WISE MEN rest and are then offered wine. Other SERVANTS start preparing a table and seats at the back of the stage.

Melchior   *(patronisingly)* Caleb, there are no comforts in the desert.
                     We knew that when we set out. We must make the best of what little we
                     have.

Caleb   Thank you, sir, you're an inspiration to us all.

Melchior   *(patronisingly – moves away)* I hope so, Caleb, I hope so.

MELCHIOR goes frontstage to join BALTHAZAR and CASPAR. CALEB goes over to organise the SERVANTS who are preparing a most lavish feast: fruits, peacocks, hog's head, candelabra, silver, napkins, flowers etc.

Balthazar   *(sipping from a silver chalice)* Melchior, come and join us.
                     What's been keeping you?

Melchior   *(taking his place and accepting another silver chalice)* Morale's a bit low
                     back there. Had to raise their spirits, but they'll be all right now.

Balthazar   *(lolling back and taking another sip)* Good man, Melchior.
                     They're not used to this: first time for most of them.

Caspar   *(standing up)* It's a grave responsibility. They depend on us.
                     Leadership and example are what they need.

Balthazar   *(as both stand up, raising a chalice)* And we shall not fail them.
                     Never have and never will!

JUST KEEP TRAVELLING ON

March tempo: mock-heroic (♩ = 110)

1. When you ven - ture out in - to the
2. We be - lieve a King has come to

de - sert and you have to face the heat and sun, and you
save us and we must be there when he ap - pears, so we'll

think you'll die of thirst and hun - ger, but you know you must go
walk on brave - ly till we find him, and ig - nore our doubts and

on.   Like a sol - dier go - ing in - to bat - tle   you must
fears.   When we saw his star rise up a - bove us   we were

ne - ver turn your back and run. You must o - ver - come all fear of
first to make the sac - ri - fice. Though we knew we'd have to face great

dan - ger till you know the job's well done.
hard - ships, we were keen to pay the price.

With a swing
All Three Kings

Chorus

Though we've jour - neyed far through de - sert sand-storms we were not a - fraid when

things went wrong, for we al - ways knew we'd see it all through if we

17

just keep tra - vel - ling on.

A magnificent banquet is now prepared.

Caleb	*(to WISE MEN)* Supper's ready, sirs, if you'd like to take your seats. *(WISE MEN turn round to see a magnificent spread)* *(apologetically to MELCHIOR)* I'm afraid, sir, this is all I could manage.
Melchior	*(unimpressed, condescendingly)* Caleb, in the circumstances, you've done remarkably well.
Caleb	Thank you, sir.

WISE MEN take their places at the table. SERVANTS serve them while looking longingly at the food and drink.

Caspar	*(filling his plate with huge helpings – to CALEB)* When we've finished, you and the servants can have what's left over.
Caleb	Thank you, sir, most considerate.
Caspar	*(taking a huge mouthful)* Not at all, Caleb, it's only right. 'Don't ask the men to do what you're not prepared to do yourself.' That's my motto.
Caleb	*(with two jugs)* Yes, sir, red or white?
Melchior	*(uninterested)* Anything, it doesn't matter.

The WISE MEN carry on feasting while the SERVANTS continue serving.

SCENE: UP IN THE SKY

Angelica — *(to SUNBEAM, out of GABRIEL'S earshot)* I'm not watching this all night. I'm off.

Sunbeam — Don't, Angelica. You'll get us all into trouble.

Angelica — Too bad. I don't care! It couldn't be worse than this.
(exit ANGELICA with the star)

Gabriel — When they have all finished their meal, we shall let them rest and then lead them on to the new-born King.

Sunbeam — Angel Gabriel . . .

Gabriel — Don't interrupt me when I'm speaking! And I want you to be on your best behaviour.

Sunbeam — Angel Gabriel . . .

Gabriel — *(annoyed)* All right, Sunbeam, what is it?

Sunbeam — Angelica's gone.

Gabriel — What do you mean, Angelica's gone?

Sunbeam — She's flown away. Look, and she's taken the star.

Gabriel — *(very cross, looking upwards)* What a disobedient little angel. Come on, we must catch her up before she gets lost in space.
(all ANGELS exit)

SCENE: DOWN BELOW

WISE MEN carry on eating and drinking while the SERVANTS continue to wait on them.

Balthazar — *(lecturing CALEB, in between gulps of wine and large mouthfuls of food)* You know, Caleb, nothing worthwhile has ever been achieved without sacrifice. Remember that.

Caleb — I'll try to, sir. *(offering dish)* Another chicken leg or some fruit and cheese?

Balthazar — *(wiping his mouth with a napkin)* No, Caleb, that's enough. Must leave something for the servants. 'Always think of others before yourself', I say.

Caleb — I know, sir.

Melchior — *(wiping his mouth with a napkin and looking upwards)* Caspar! Balthazar! Look! The star's appeared again and is moving west! We have to go.

Balthazar — *(to SERVANTS)* Quick, clear the tables! Catch us up as soon as you can!

WISE MEN get up. CARRIERS bring out 'chairs'. WISE MEN move off. SERVANTS hastily remove tables and leftovers and take them offstage.

SCENE: THE INN AT BETHLEHEM

Enter INNKEEPER and COMPANIONS, with barrels of wine.

Innkeeper	*(to others)* Right, put those barrels over there and top 'em up with water. No one's gonna know.

COMPANIONS pour buckets of water into the barrels. One COMPANION is writing prices on a slate. INNKEEPER rushes over to him, grabs slate and wipes out the writing.

Innkeeper	No, bed and breakfast, twenty shekels, not five! Wine, sixteen. Supper, twenty-five!
Reuben	Ain't that a bit steep, guv?
Innkeeper	Reuben, my boy, half the world's coming to Bethlehem to be counted. There won't be room for everyone. We can charge what we like. *(enter COOK, sidestage with two scraggy chickens)*
Cook	*(deadpan)* What am I supposed to do with these? They wouldn't make a chicken sandwich.
Innkeeper	*(irritably)* Use yer loaf, Arkhim. Stick in a few dead crows and a couple of pigeons. All looks the same in a stew. *(COOK leaves, po-faced)* *(to ARAM, tersely)* Aram, take the luggage. Nice and respectful. Then we'll go through it when they've all gone to bed.
Hazar	And I charge them double for service, when they've all had their supper?
Innkeeper	*(very pleased)* Good boy, Hazar. Yer learning. *(re-enter COOK with two small bags of flour)*
Cook	*(matter-of-fact)* I can't make fifty loaves from two bags of flour. It's impossible.
Innkeeper	Arkhim, there's loads of sawdust around the back. Do I 'ave to tell yer everything? *(exit COOK, enter HIRAM)*
Hiram	*(to INNKEEPER)* I done what yer said, guv. Done up the top rooms and got rid of the rats.
Innkeeper	Well done, Hiram, can't be too careful. *(re-enter COOK with a basket of apples)*
Cook	*(miserably)* I can't make apple pies out of these. They're all rotten.
Innkeeper	Arkhim, can't yer see I'm busy? Why are yer worrying me? Put 'em in the stew. It all adds up. *(exit COOK)* *(excitedly)* We'll make a fortune tomorrow. We'll be living in luxury after this.
Hiram	Unless we get caught. Then we'll be in prison for the rest of our lives.
Innkeeper	No chance of that, Hiram. I'm far too clever.

SOMETHING FOR A RAINY DAY

24

Innkeeper	*(looking into the distance)* Hey, look sharp! First guests are coming up the road. This could be a nice little earner by the looks of 'em. *(enter WISE MEN)*
Balthazar	Greetings, sir. I wonder if you can help us?
Innkeeper	*(bowing)* Anything you want. Single rooms, double rooms, full board, half board. We're at your service.
Caspar	We're three travellers from Persia. We've been following a star that led us all the way here.
Innkeeper	I'm not surprised. This is the best hotel in Bethlehem!
Melchior	We weren't intending to stay. *(looking around)* No offence, but *(pause)* it's not quite five-star, if you know what I mean.
Balthazar	We're looking for the new-born King of Israel. We thought you might know where we could find him.
Innkeeper	No problem. He's in Herod's palace. First turning on the right when you get to Jerusalem. They've been celebrating all night.
Melchior	Thank you so much. We are most grateful.
Innkeeper	Anything we can do to help. Enjoy yourselves. *(bows)* *(exit WISE MEN)* Cor, I'd love to be a fly on the wall when they tell Herod they're looking for a new-born king!
Hiram	That's wicked, guv. You shouldn't do things like that.
Innkeeper	Serve them right. Too snooty to stay in a place like this.
Hiram	*(looking sidestage)* Look, guv. Two more coming. I'll see to 'em. *(goes to sidestage)* Welcome to 'Palm Tree Lodge'. Anything you need, you'll find it here. *(enter JOSEPH and MARY)*
Joseph	Thank you. My name is Joseph, from Nazareth in Galilee. This is my wife, Mary.
Hiram	*(shaking hands with JOSEPH)* Pleased to meet you, Joseph. *(gives MARY a respectful nod)* Ma'am.
Joseph	We're looking for a room for the night.

Hiram	I've got just the thing. Top floor, lovely view.
Joseph	It doesn't matter about the view, so long as it's private. *(pause)* You see, Mary is expecting a child any moment now.
Hiram	Then, I'll give you a room right at the back.
Innkeeper	*(moves over, very concerned. Speaks to HIRAM)* Wait a minute, Hiram. I'm running a business here, not a clinic. *(to MARY, kindly)* Sorry, love, if you're having a baby, you can't stay here.
Joseph	We've tried everywhere else. They're all full up.
Innkeeper	*(after a short hesitation)* Look, tell you what, I've got a little cattle shed just down the road. You can stay there and it'll cost yer nothing.
Joseph	Thank you, that would suit us fine.
Innkeeper	You're welcome, mate. Take 'em down there, Hiram. Make sure they're nice and warm and they've got everything they want.

HIRAM leads MARY and JOSEPH off stage.

Hazar	*(looking sidestage)* Look, now they're coming. Dozens of 'em.
Innkeeper	*(looking sidestage)* Lady Luck! Never thought I'd see anything like this! *(to ALL)* Come on then! Help 'em with their luggage. Can't miss out on this one. *(ALL exit)*

SCENE: UP IN THE SKY

Enter ANGELS, led by ANGEL GABRIEL who is carrying the star

Gabriel	*(curtly)* Right, sit down. You're all in disgrace!

ANGEL GABRIEL and the other ANGELS sit in silence for a while.

Stardust	*(to ANGELICA)* This is all *your* fault, you know.
Gabriel	*(curtly)* I said – no talking.
Gloria	Well, it's not fair. She always spoils everything.
Twilight	She thinks she can do what she likes, even in heaven.

Gabriel	*(curtly)* You're all the same. I'll never take you out again.
Sunbeam	*(to crestfallen ANGELICA)* There, see what you've done. Now we'll be sent back to heaven, singing hymns and playing harps all day long.
Angelica	*(spitefully)* You couldn't play a harp if you practised for ever.
Gabriel	*(exasperated)* Right, that's it! I'm taking you to Herod's palace. Maybe this will teach you a lesson. *(pause – sternly)* Come on! I want you to be there before the Wise Men arrive.

Exit ANGEL GABRIEL followed by grumbling ANGELS.

SCENE: THE DRESSING ROOM IN HEROD'S PALACE

Enter DRESSERS and ATTENDANTS. Two place a large throne at one side of the stage. Another places a large mirror opposite. Others carry crowns, cloaks, scissors, combs etc. When ALL are ready and waiting, enter KING HEROD. ALL bow. SERVANTS start dressing HEROD while making occasional gestures of hatred behind his back – clenched fists, poking out tongues etc.

Herod	*(pompously)* Don't be too long this evening. The banquet starts in half an hour.
Mr Zedechiah	*(standing behind the throne)* If you would graciously sit here, sire, I'm sure we'll have you ready in a very short time.

HEROD sits on the throne. MR ZEDECHIAH starts 'doing' his hair. Fussing, combing, dabbing on oils, and snipping very small pieces of hair here and there.

Shemiah	*(producing a beautiful cape and showing it to HEROD)* May I suggest white satin tonight, sire, edged with pure gold braid. It's our latest design.
Herod	*(giving it just one glance)* No, far too plain. I'm a king, not a courtier.
Jozabad	*(producing another beautiful cape and showing it to HEROD)* Then perhaps you'd prefer this delightful cape of blended colours. It took us three years to get it just right.
Herod	*(glances, hesistates for a moment)* No, too gaudy. I'm supposed to look regal.
Zabdiel	*(producing a third beautiful cape and showing it to HEROD)* Then, King Herod, I think we have just the thing. Purple silk with ermine trim.

Herod	*(standing up)* I think I might try that. *(he puts on the cape and views himself in the mirror from various angles)* *(to ALL)* What do you think?
Shemiah	Magnificent, King Herod.
Jozabad	Very impressive, very regal.
Zabdiel	A fitting robe for a gracious king. May your kingdom last a thousand years and a thousand days.
Herod	My kingdom, Zabdiel, will last for ever.
Zabdiel	*(pompously, but sycophantically)* Of that, sire, we have no doubt at all.
Herod	*(returns to his throne)* Now my sceptre and crown. It's nearly time for the banquet.
Jozabad	*(snapping fingers)* Zabdi! Zerah! The royal sceptre and crown.

Enter SERVANT ZABDI with crown, glittering with jewels, on a red cushion and SERVANT ZERAH with sceptre on a purple cushion. They kneel before HEROD. SHEMIAH solemnly places crown on HEROD'S head and places sceptre in his hand. Enter CAPTAIN EZRA-HADID-MAT-TANIAH.

Captain E-H-M	*(solemnly)* Three visitors from the Court of Persia to see you, sire. Shall I let them through?
Herod	*(admiring himself in the mirror)* No, can't you see I'm busy?
Captain E-H-M	*(aloof)* They say they've brought gold to give to the king.
Herod	*(hesitates)* I'll give them a minute. No, more! Show them in.

Exit CAPTAIN EZRA-HADID-MATTANIAH. He returns with the WISE MEN.

Balthazar	Great King Herod. We are three travellers from the east – Caspar, Melchior and . . .
Herod	Cut the speeches. Just leave the gold in the corner and be off. I have important duties to perform.
Caspar	But the gold is for the new-born King, foretold by the prophets.
Melchior	We've been following a star that stopped over Bethlehem but now it's disappeared.
Herod	That's a shame. *I've* been looking for him too. If you find him let me know, then I can go and worship him.
Balthazar	*(bowing)* Rest assured, your Majesty, if we find him, you will be the first to know. *(exit WISE MEN)*

Herod

(to ALL) Go and tell the guards to follow those men. I don't trust them.
(to CAPTAIN E-H-M) And, Captain, see to it that all baby boys in
Bethlehem under three are put to the sword before midnight.
*(ALL exit. HEROD goes nearer to the mirror and admires himself
from various angles)*
(Speaks to mirror) Oh yes, Herod, you are magnificent. I worship you.
*(HEROD looks around him to see that no one is looking
and sings to the mirror)*

WON-WON-WONDERFUL!

30

29

Weal-thy, cle-ver and world-ly-wise, you are no-bo-dy's fool. It's
He-rod, look a-round high and low, all is un-der your rule. You're

2nd time to Coda

33

not sur-pris-ing you've come this far, you're won-won-won-der-ful!
migh-ty, pow-er-ful lord of all, you're

Enter CAPTAIN, unseen by HEROD. He watches in amazement.

Dance

37

41

45

Captain E-H-M	*(coughs discreetly, trying to attract HEROD'S attention)* Hmmm, hmmm, dinner is served, your majesty. The guests are waiting for you.
Herod	*(Regaining his composure and dignity)* Yes, of course, Captain. Lead the way and tell them to sound the trumpets. *(exit HEROD, led by CAPTAIN E-H-M)*

SCENE: UP IN THE SKY

Enter ANGELS, led by ANGEL GABRIEL. ALL sit down.

Stardust	What a horrible man!
Gloria	I never thought humans could be so nasty.
Gabriel	Herod has always been nasty and selfish, ever since he was a little boy. Now he's grown old in his ways, hated by all and very unhappy inside.
Angelica	*(with a shudder)* I hope I'll never grow up like that!
Gabriel	*(firmly, but kindly)* But you will if you carry on like this. You'll all grow up just like Herod.
Twilight	*(enthusiastically)* I'll never be like Herod! From now on, I'm going to be kind to everyone.
Moonshine	*(enthusiastically)* And I'm going to help all those humans down below.
Rainbow	And I'm never going to be selfish again.
Angelica	*(very enthusiastically)* And when I get back to heaven, I'm going to sing songs of praise all day and all night!
Gabriel	*(not entirely impressed)* All right, don't overdo it. I'll be quite happy if you just stop fighting for a while.
Angelica	*(enthusiastically and sincerely)* Angel Gabriel, we'll never fight again. We're going to be good angels from now on.
Gabriel	*(pause, then gently)* Promise?
Angels	*(firmly)* Promise!
Gabriel	Then I'll let you give the good news to those poor shepherds down below. *(ANGELS join hands and watch)*

SCENE: THE SHEPHERDS' FIELD

Enter SHEPHERDS, consoling AKKUB.

Hasshub	*(with arms around AKKUB)* Cheer up, Akkub, you can worship God out in the fields.
Akkub	*(still upset and distressed)* I only wanted to say my prayers.
Hasshub	We know, Akkub, but shepherds aren't allowed into the Temple. We told you before you went down there.
Akkub	*(still distressed)* That high priest was really snobby. He told me I was unclean and never washed.
Zabdi	Don't worry about it, Akkub. God still loves you.
Akkub	Nobody loves us. We're just poor shepherds. No one cares about us at all.

SCENE: UP IN THE SKY

Angelica	Poor shepherds. Why won't they let them into the Temple?
Gabriel	Because they're outcasts. They're supposed to be unclean. Up here in the hills they can't follow all the holy rules.
Stardust	Doesn't anybody like them?
Gabriel	God does, and I think it's about time we went down and told them.

GLORY TO GOD

Lively calypso ($\boldsymbol{\downarrow}$ = 172)

Glo - ry to God, *(claps)* glo - ry to God, *(claps)*

glo - ry, glo - ry, glo - ry to God in the high - est.

3rd time to Coda

Glo - ry to God, *(claps)* glo - ry to God, *(claps)*

SCENE: DOWN BELOW IN THE SHEPHERDS' FIELD

Hasshub   *(excitedly)* I can't believe it! The Son of God has come to live with us!

Akkhub   And sent his angels to tell us first!

Zabdi   *(enthusiastically)* Then let's go and meet him!
Let's go and greet the new-born King! *(the SHEPHERDS rush off stage)*

SCENE: UP IN THE SKY

Gabriel   Now it's time for *us* to greet the new-born King. Just take it gently,
open wings, softly up and down. *(looking back at ANGELS)*
That's lovely, just right. Now we'll glide gently down to earth.

Music (see over) begins as ANGELS exit slowly and gently. The music continues as the next scene is set and, as required, under the following dialogue.

NATIVITY MUSIC

SCENE: THE STABLE AT BETHLEHEM

A small stool and manger are placed sidestage. Enter JOSEPH and MARY carrying the 'baby'. MARY stands to centre and cuddles the baby. JOSEPH takes stool and manger to centrestage. MARY sits down with JOSEPH beside her. She places the baby in the manger. Enter SHEPHERDS with lambs. Very quietly, they go up to the manger and place the lamb before the baby.

Akkub   Holy Child, Lord and God, welcome to the world.

Enter WISE MEN; very quietly and respectfully, they go up to the manger and offer gifts.

Balthazar   Holy Child, Lord and King, we bring you gifts from the east. Gold . . .

Caspar   Frankincense . . .

Melchior   And myrrh.

Enter INNKEEPER and COMPANIONS

Innkeeper   Holy Child, we have nothing to offer you. My inn is full tonight but the rich didn't come, only the poor, the sick and the lonely.
We're sorry we had no room for you.

Joseph   Then you gave us all a room. Whatever you did for the poor, you did for Jesus.

ALL bow down and reverently adore the Child Jesus when suddenly there is a very loud crashing sound offstage. Dialogue follows offstage, clearly audible.

Gabriel   Oh no! Can't you get anything right? What a way to land!

Sunbeam   It's her fault, she pushed me.

Angelica   She got in my way!

Gabriel   And you! Look at the state of your wings!
Trust you to land in a muddy puddle.

Twilight   Serves her right. Showing off, she was.

Moonshine   At least I landed the right way up. Not like some . . . *(pauses abruptly)*
We're doing it again – fighting and being horrid to each other. I'm sorry.
(the other ANGELS apologise, their speeches overlapping:
'I'm sorry too', 'We didn't mean to break our promise', 'We forgot',
'Please forgive us', etc.)

Gabriel   We haven't got time to clean you up, so you'll just have to go in as you are.
And please . . . try to look holy for a change!

Enter ANGELS while introductory music of song plays. They look bedraggled and the worse for wear but also, genuinely holy and contrite. Some with hands together, prayerfully, and some with arms crossed on their chest, hands on shoulders.

ANGELS UP HIGH

KEVIN MAYHEW PERFORMANCE LICENCE FORM

We are delighted that you are considering *Angels up high* for production.
Please note that a performance licence is required and royalties are payable as follows:

10% of gross takings, plus VAT
(Minimum fee: £15.00 + VAT = £17.63)

This form should be returned to the Copyright Department at Kevin Mayhew Ltd. A copy, including our performance licence number, will be returned to you.

Name of Organisation _____

Contact name _____

Contact address _____

_____

Postcode _____

Contact Telephone No. _____ Contact Fax No. _____

E-mail _____

Date(s) of performance(s) _____

Venue _____

Seating capacity _____

Proposed ticket price _____

I undertake to submit performance fees due to Kevin Mayhew Ltd within 28 days of the last performance of *Angels up high*, together with a statement of gross takings.

Signature _____

Name (please print) _____

On behalf of _____

Address if different from above _____

_____

To be completed by Kevin Mayhew Copyright Department:

Performance Licence No. _____ is issued to _____

for _____ performances of *Angels up high* on _____

Copyright Department, Kevin Mayhew Ltd, Buxhall, Stowmarket, Suffolk, IP14 3BW
Telephone number: UK 01449 737978   International +44 1449 737978
Fax number: UK 01449 737834   International +44 1449 737834
E-mail: info@kevinmayhewltd.com